MOBY DICK

HERMAN MELVILLE

Adapted by Dr. Marion Kimberly

GALLERY BOOKS
An Imprint of W. H. Smith Publishers Inc.
112 Madison Avenue
New York City 10016

© 1990 Ediciones B, S.A., Barcelona, Spain

This edition published 1991 by Gallery Books,
an imprint of W.H.Smith Publishers, Inc.,
112 Madison Avenue, New York, New York 10016

ISBN 0-8317-1457-3

Gallery Books are available for bulk purchase for sales
promotions and premium use. For details write or telephone
the Manager of Special Sales, W.H.Smith Publishers, Inc.,
112 Madison Avenue, New York, New York 10016. (212) 532-6600

Produced by Hawk Books Limited, London

Printed in Spain

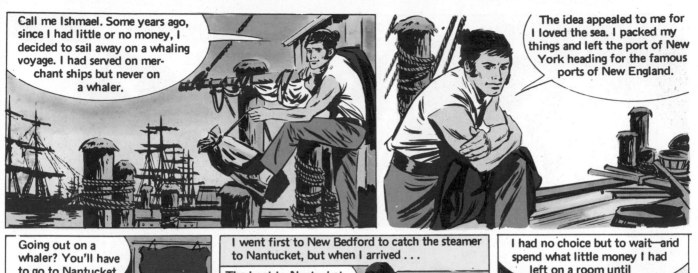

Call me Ishmael. Some years ago, since I had little or no money, I decided to sail away on a whaling voyage. I had served on merchant ships but never on a whaler.

The idea appealed to me for I loved the sea. I packed my things and left the port of New York heading for the famous ports of New England.

Going out on a whaler? You'll have to go to Nantucket. The whaling vessels set to sea from there.

I went first to New Bedford to catch the steamer to Nantucket, but when I arrived . . .

The boat to Nantucket has left already. You'll have to wait until Monday.

I had no choice but to wait—and spend what little money I had left on a room until Monday.

You need a room? Sorry my lad we're full up. The last room I had has been taken by a gentleman who is a harpoonist. Well . . .

Just a minute. It has a big bed. You can share it with him, if you don't mind.

I don't really care to, but if you don't have anything else, I guess I have no choice.

I had a small supper and went right to bed.

I hope I'm lucky and get aboard one of these whaling ships in Nantucket. I don't have much money and I need a job.

Well, it's time I got some sleep.

1

I had just turned out the light when . . .

Oh, boy! Look at my bed partner! He looks like a real character. I wonder where he came from.

What do you want here? This is my room. Speak up or I'll kill you!

Stop! I've had enough trouble for one day.

Since he was coming at me with a large knife . . .

Landlord! Help! Come here! Now!

I'm being attacked by a savage! Help! All I wanted to do was to get a good night's sleep.

Don't be afraid now. Queequeg here wouldn't hurt a hair on your head. He's really a very gentle man.

Oh, me not know you guest here. Me no hurt you. Me Queequeg — harpoonist. It is good to shake your hand, friend.

P-p-pleased to meet you.

I came here from New York but missed the steamer to Nantucket. You said you're a whaler, Queequeg?

That's right, friend. Maybe we be shipmates? You and me smoke big pipe of friendship now.

OK, thanks. My name is Ishmael. I want to ship aboard a whaler. I'm going to try to find a ship in Nantucket.

②

Queequeg began telling his story. He was born on Kokovoko, an island far to the Southwest. His father was a chief.

Whaling is new to me. I'm anxious to get to sea.

I stowed away on big boat. Became great harpoonist. Looking now for work on whaler.

Have no work for long time. We look together, Okay? Find jobs aboard good whaling ship.

Great! Maybe they'll hire us in Nantucket.

So that's how I met Queequeg and how we happened to set off for work together

Ho! Ho! That savage is your friend?

Ha,ha,ha!

Ha, ha! What a strange-looking one he is!

You miserable son of a sea cook . . . .

I teach you big lesson, you . . .

No, no! Captain, help! This man is going to kill me!

AAGH....!

The only man aboard who can't swim and you have to pick on him. Take it easy fellow.

Help! I'm drowning! Somebody help me! I can't swim! Glub . . . Glub . . . Help!

Without saying a word, Queequeg took his clothes off, and . . .

I save him.

③

That is a man of great courage!

He saved the man who made fun of him! Not many men would do such a thing.

He's not really so bad-looking. And even if he was he is a real shipmate. I'd be proud to sail with him.

That's a beautiful example to follow, men. The dangers of the sea can bring out the best in a man.

The rest of the crossing to Nantucket was uneventful. The next day . . .

Do you think anyone will hire us? I want to get back to the sea.

I think so, friend.

Look at that whaler. Let's try luck there. We will find work.

Wait a minute. It's better to jump into the sea with a stone around your neck than sail on the PEQUOD.

What do you mean by that, friend?

Captain Ahab of the PEQUOD carries with him a strange, evil spell. It's bad to sail with him.

That's nonsense. We need work. We ask for it here. No evil spell on Captain. PEQUOD good ship.

Don't say I didn't warn you. Did you know Captain Ahab lost a leg?

It was eaten by a giant white whale!

Let's go. Don't listen to him. We can take care of ourselves.

Go back, you fools! Go back before it's too late! No good will come from a voyage on that cursed ship, not with Captain Ahab!

4

Excuse me, sir. Are you the captain? We'd like to work here. My friend has whaling experience.

No, I'm not the captain. I'm first officer Starbuck. So you'd like to work aboard the PEQUOD, huh?

I showed him my papers and he seemed interested, but . . .

Not him. He doesn't even speak! You seem like a whaler, but this savage has no papers and doesn't talk!

He's the best harpoonist in the world.

Ho, ho! Don't make me laugh! Him a harpoonist? That savage? I never heard anything so funny in all my life!

You laugh? You see that drop of tar out there? If that were a whale . . .

You mean that little speck?

At that moment Queequeg took a harpoon he saw on deck, took aim, and . . .

Look. You see the drop of tar now?

My God! He hit it with the harpoon!

Good job. You're hired. You are an expert harpoonist.

Hurray!

THE PEQUOD was sailing at dawn. Queequeg and I went down to the dock to celebrate.

It's you fellows again. I hope you paid attention and gave up sailing on this boat.

No, sir. You're mistaken.

⑤

Of course. You saw me in the bar in New Bedford, remember? That wasn't so long ago. Ha. Ha.

As for you, you'll be my number one harpoonist.

That's alright with me Mr. Starbuck.

You're Tashtego, right? You'll be my harpoonist.

And you'll be mine. What's your name?

Daggoo, Mr. Flask.

Good luck, friend. I'm an American Indian.

Thanks, I'm an African, Tashtego.

I'm Queequeg. Good luck, Tashtego, Daggoo.

Good luck, Queequeg.

Luck from me, too.

It was already broad daylight when . . .

I'll bet anything that's the mysterious Captain Ahab at last.

I had guessed correctly. I could tell that this man, who walked with a leg made of whale's jawbone, had a heart which. . .

. . . was filled with a strange sadness.

Notice how he looks at the sun — almost as if he were trying to get even with it.

I didn't realize how close to the truth I was in my feelings.

You stop thinking now. Come with me. We have drink together.

The first days' journeys were uneventful, until one morning . . .

What?

Look alive, you loafers! Keep watch!
There are whales out there!

You've heard we've sighted
whales! I'm telling you there's
a monster
out there
. . .

With three holes in her tail.
She's big and she's white.
If you see her, yell!

Is that the
one they call
Moby Dick?

I've never heard of a white whale!
The captain sounds as if he
knows this white whale
very well.

There really
is one, and it's the
one Captain Ahab is
looking for.

Listen, men. What I'm telling you is true. There is an enormous monster of a white whale who is Captain Ahab's
nightmare.

What do you think of
this, Starbuck?

Just another
lie — one of the many
stories that Captain
Ahab tells.

At that moment the whales swam quietly away, and
in a little while . . .

Tell the
crew to stand
at attention,
Officer Starbuck.

Listen, men. I
suppose some of you
don't believe me when
I tell of the great white
whale. Unless you follow
my orders to the letter
you will be sorry!

8

I speak the truth. Such a creature does live in some parts of the ocean. . . and it will die at my hands — I swear it! Now get back to work, you sea going loafers!

But first — you see this gold coin? It's worth 16 dollars and it. . . .

. . .goes to the first man who sights Moby Dick, the great white whale!

See my leg! It was Moby Dick who ruined it! I'll follow that creature to the end of the world, if I must. To catch it is the purpose of this trip.

The words of Captain Ahab fired up the crew.

A harpoon for the monster!

I'll win the gold!

Hurrah, Captain Ahab!

Are you afraid to try, Starbuck? I hope I won't be sorry I hired you as first mate on the PEQUOD.

A double order of rum for everyone now! Drink! There are rough days ahead.

The men were happy with Captain Ahab's latest order. We drank, and from that moment the strongest wish of every man aboard was to sight and to capture the great white whale.

I heard in Nantucket that the captain has been planning this voyage for a long time.

I noticed that once we sighted a whale the captain ordered the boat lowered and . . .

He, himself, went out with three harpoonists to chase it down.

Row faster, men. It's the white whale, MOBY DICK!

9

She's ours! We've got her! Curse that monster! I'll have my revenge.

But the whale attacked and.....

AAAGH..!

Something like this happened before. Only the captain and two men lived through it for the whale attacked the whaling ship.

And sunk it, too?

That's, that's horrible!

The ship, which was twice the size of the PEQUOD, was shattered.

This is all true, Ishmael. I know story of Captain Ahab, and that great white whale.

What?

Why didn't you tell me? We should have listened to those men in Nantucket who warned us.

I not want to scare you. I want to sail with you — make you good whaler. Come, I tell you story now.

You know how he lost leg? I was there. Not many men lived. Here is how it happened. One day....

Captain Ahab's ship came by monster whale.

Lower the long boats! Quickly!

He got in one boat.

Ready. Ready, harpoonists! Aim carefully now, she's a big one.

We came close to whale.

Captain, she's turning into us! She's going to hit us!

In the name of the devil, closer!

AAAAH!....

Then the animal tear off captain's leg.

I'll get even with you some day, you monster! I swear it!

And this is all he's looking for? He doesn't care about whaling for a profit. He only wants to get even with that whale who took his leg.

That right, friend. That true story of captain.

From that time on, the captain's entire purpose was to hunt down the whale. He was like a madman in his search . . .

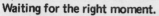

Waiting for the right moment.

One night, one of the sailors who was carrying water for the next day's use...

Shhh! Don't make so much noise. Can't you hear . . .

I don't hear anything. Stop talking such non-sense!

It's not nonsense. There—under the hatches—don't you hear it—a cough—it sounded like a cough.

You're crazy. The noise you hear is your stomach growling from the big meal you just ate. There's really nothing to hear. Get back to work.

11

Meanwhile, in his cabin, Captain Ahab spent the night planning new sailing routes on the ship's maps.

Now I have it. I'll go around Cape Horn and into the Pacific Ocean. I'll get up near the equator in time to hunt that monster. Moby Dick can't hide from me much longer.

This will be my chance to get even. I'll get her at last! I can recognize Moby Dick in an ocean of whales.

He couldn't sleep from thinking about it. He walked on deck for hours, staring out into the ocean.

The plan took hold of him and he could think of nothing else.

One hot afternoon as the sailors were just sitting around . . .

A - A - AHOY!

That's Tashtego's call. He's on watch.

Huh?

Over there! Whales in sight! Look! Over there! See a whole school of whales!

To your posts, men. Harpoonists, to the long boats. There's no time to lose.

At that exact moment without warning . . .

These men! They're the ones I heard coughing the other night!

Where do you suppose they came from?

⑫

They're Malaysians. The captain hired them secretly. He's said nothing to anyone about them.

Starbuck, the first mate, saw the five strangers and . . .

Captain, you owe us an explanation. Who are these men, where did they come from, and why are they aboard?

That's my business, not yours, Mr. Starbuck!

I'm the captain of this ship. Those men are not sailors, but they claim they will help us hunt Moby Dick. Enough now, go to your posts.

The boats were lowered, then . . .

Who can these men be? Why did the captain take them on without telling anyone?

Shove off! Let's get going. Pull hard on those oars!

Look over there. The captain took the Malaysians into his long boat. He's heading straight for the whales. They'll get there first.

It was true.

Row, men! She's already ours. Be quick and I'll buy each of you a ranch in California.

One of these five men seemed to have a very strong influence over Captain Ahab.

No, it's not Moby Dick. Not yet. But we're on the right track.

Thanks, Fedallah. But remember, just do your job. That's why I brought you along.

So you can guide me to Moby Dick through the advice of your oracle.

We came near to the whales as the sky was darkening. At that moment the first whale appeared.

Oh, no! A northeast wind! That means we're in for some bad weather.

No matter. Go on. After them! They must not get away!

Give it to him, Queequeg! Jam that harpoon home! Don't miss!

Queequeg was the only one close enough to throw the harpoon, but . . .

CAREFUL!

One of the whales just managed to upset our boat before swimming away with the rest.

Uh! We're having bad luck, men.

A storm. That's all we need!

The rest of the harpoonists could do nothing. We were lucky to get back to the ship an hour later.

Hoist all the sails now. Quickly!

Ohh! Does it always go like this on whalers, Queequeg?

Not always, but sometimes happens. I think it bad luck ship, Ishmael. Bad luck. We lucky. We still alive.

We were helped back on board. When a count of the men was made, it was found that two were missing.

Bad luck. Those Malaysians — it's their fault.

From then on the strange Fedallah became even more mysterious. What hold did this man have over Captain Ahab?

What rotten luck! Not a single whale, Fedallah, not a one! We must not fail. Moby Dick must be found.

Do not be afraid. We are on the right track, Captain. My oracle never fails.

Several uneventful days passed at sea. Then . . .

Whale in sight! There she blows! Whale in sight off to the left. She's spouting.

14

All hands on deck. Unfurl the sails. Quickly, men, we must catch up with the whale.

There was no mistake. We saw the whale off in the distance.

It's true. See over there, Ishmael?

We sailed after it at top speed, but couldn't catch it. It was getting away.

It has to be her. What rotten luck! That has to be Moby Dick.

We chased it for several hours until the sailors began to worry.

Don't you see? She is leading us on out here. She has plans for us.

Later she'll turn and tear us apart. That's the way Moby Dick operates.

Captain, we don't think we should go on.

It's madness to do so.

If this is Moby Dick, she's planning to kill us.

I don't want to hear any more of this talk. Back to your posts, or I'll string you up like we do the whales! I am Captain here.

Stay at your post, pilot, and stay on the course I charted. We may have to sail around the world, but I will kill Moby Dick.

I think the captain is crazy, Queequeg. God help us on this voyage! No man is safe on a ship commanded by a madman.

The days passed slowly and we continued sailing. Then one morning Daggoo, the harpoonist, thought he saw. . .

Huh? No, it's not possible!

Over there, to starboard. She blows! She blows! Whale in sight.

AT LAST! AT LAST! We've found her.

Moby Dick! This time it's really Moby Dick! Lower the long boats!

Was Captain Ahab really sure of what he saw?

The boats were launched once more.

Come on, men. Hurry up! Don't be afraid. Just go!

But two hours later, where the captain thought he saw Moby Dick . . .

Turn around, men! Turn and row for the PEQUOD — fast!

It big octopus! Men who see it never come back.

16

Queequeg — harpoon him! We only have one chance to get him, or he'll get us.

The harpoon hit its mark and the immense octopus sank slowly to the bottom of the sea.

The whale has gone. Let's hurry back on board the ship.

The four boats returned to the PEQUOD where, once more, the crew began grumbling.

No doubt about it, those Malaysians have brought bad luck.

Not one whale since we left Nantucket.

The ship is cursed.

But the next day brought a change for all heard the man on watch shout

Whale in sight — spouting to port!

Lower the boats. We'll see if our luck is better this time. The men will be glad to hunt the whale.

For the first time that trip, Lady Luck smiled on us, the whalers of the PEQUOD, because an hour later . . .

She's yours, Tashtego! Yours!

Careful with your hands there. Let's go help him out.

After a wild run, we finally stopped the whale. Stubb sank his spear into her and we towed her back to the PEQUOD.

Now you see first time what we do with whale, Ishmael.

To bad it wasn't Moby Dick, but any whale is better than none, right, Starbuck?

17

Immediately the ship became a slaughterhouse. First Starbuck and Stubb cut a large hole in the body of the whale . . .

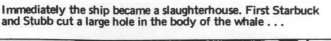

In order to put in a giant hook so it could be raised up for cutting.

The entire crew was busy for many hours at the task of cutting up the whale.

Good job, boys. You each get a double shot of rum!

In a few days the PEQUOD captured another big whale.

Hurrah!

We were so busy we almost forgot about Fedallah and his friends.

Curse the luck! Why doesn't Moby Dick come around?

You're headed right. My oracle speaks the truth.

Have you noticed, Queequeg, that Fedallah keeps talking to the captain about an oracle? That's why he's along — to make magic.

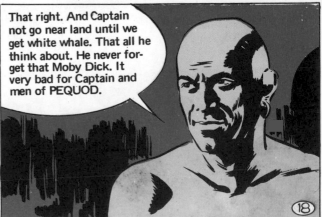

That right. And Captain not go near land until we get white whale. That all he think about. He never forget that Moby Dick. It very bad for Captain and men of PEQUOD.

It was clear that this was so. Even though the PEQUOD was having good luck and her hold was filled with whale oil, Captain Ahab's mind was still set on one thing . . .

Head for the Strait of Sunda, Starbuck. We'll sail into the Java Sea. There, I'm sure I'll find what I'm looking for . . . .

This crazy man is taking us to the end of the earth!

You know what, Stubb? I don't think we're ever going to run across that cursed white whale.

Several days later, as we neared the Strait of Sunda . . .

Hey, look here, men! Unfurl the sails and follow these whales! Moby Dick is here!

Whales too far away, Ishmael. We never catch them. We must wait for a sighting closer to ship.

As the PEQUOD followed the flock, we noticed a French whaling ship.

It's the ROSEBUD, sir. They've caught whales. I can smell them from here!

Yes, the rascals are loaded.

The French whaler is hauling two huge dead whales, Captain. The smell is awful.

Fools! Show-offs!

Stubb! I have a plan to make them let the two whales loose. Come here. Mr. Stubb! I'll need your help.

You speak French, don't you? Get in a boat and take a message to the ROSEBUD's captain.

Yes, sir. And what is the message?

Half an hour later, all ready to speak with the French whaler . . .

19

Hello, sir. I have a warning from my Captain. Yesterday he spoke with a German whaler. His men had cholera...

What? Oh, no!

They caught it from whales like the ones you're towing. The Captain thought you should be warned, sir.

Horrors!

Hurry, men. Cut those creatures loose and let's sail away from here!

And so, thanks to this clever trick, the PEQUOD gained a lot of whale oil and wax without having to work for it.

Ha, ha, fools! How could they be so dumb as to fall for that trick.

You know, Queequeg, if it weren't for this stupid search for Moby Dick, working for Captain Ahab could be a pleasure.

Two weeks later we came upon the SAMUEL ENDERBY, an English whaler. Captain Ahab went aboard to ask . . .

Have I seen Moby Dick? Captain, she may have taken your leg, but she took my arm! That was enough for me.

Since then I've kept clear of the beast! Last time I saw her, she was heading east, but it was around here. If I were you Captain, I wouldn't want to meet Moby Dick again.

When Captain Ahab returned . . .

Mr. Starbuck, at last we have something to go on. Set a course toward the East. Immediately!

20

I already told you that before you die, and on this voyage, you'll see one or two funeral cars — one not made by humans, the other of American wood.

Suddenly we heard a scream.

Man overboard!

A barrel, which served as a safety float, was thrown, but . . .

How will he save himself if the barrel fills up with water?

The PEQUOD had another victim.

We must look for a better float.

I have something.

Queequeg went below. Soon . . .

I had it built for my coffin a long time ago.

Good, we'll waterproof it and keep it handy.

Ho, ho! If the ship should sink, it would be a sight to watch thirty men fight for a place on this box!   Ha, ha, ha!

Our voyage continued with nothing unusual happening. Sometimes we would see another whaler.

It's the RACHEL, sir. The captain's son was lost in a boat. He'd like us to help look for him.

Tell him no, Starbuck. I can't waste time looking for anyone.

You never have time for anything but that cursed whale. You're sick, Captain Ahab.

22

One day we came across a whaler who . . .

Have I seen Moby Dick? Look what she did to my boats! I'd like to put an end to that monster once and for all!

Really? Then look at this harpoon! Forged by lightning and warmed with blood! It's going to kill Moby Dick!

The PEQUOD sailed on . . .

You look worried, Ishmael. What the matter?

I have a funny feeling, Queequeg...

A feeling that we're headed for a lot of trouble.

The next morning that feeling was going to come true.

Why are you up so early, Captain?

I've checked the ship's course, Starbuck. We've got to be close to the monster.

If it weren't that I feel we're all going to perish, I'd laugh like a madman. His head is filled up with this non-sense.

Good morning, Starbuck. What's the captain doing up so early?

Just look at him, Stubb. He is trying to get a glimpse of Moby Dick.

I'm tired of this. Today I'm heading the PEQUOD back to Nantucket.

Good idea. I'm with you. We've got all the whale oil we can carry. It's crazy to stay out here.

Suddenly a scream like thunder from the skies echoed throughout the ship.

IT'S HER!

㉓

MOBY DICK!

MOBY DICK AT LAST!

In a moment all the men were on deck.

She's enormous!

It's her, Fedallah! Moby Dick at last! The oracle has done it!

Prepare the harpoons! Launch the boats, Mister Starbuck.

The order was carried out at once.

Minutes later . . .

GET GOING, MEN! WE'LL GET HER THIS TIME!

Oh, cursed one! Your hour has come!

The whaling boats came nearer to the huge whale, but . . .

Tell everyone she's disappeared! But she'll be up again in a minute!

Watch out, men. Be prepared for her. She'll be coming up . . . . .

The captain was not mistaken. In a few minutes she came up. I could see that he had guessed correctly. It was indeed Moby Dick, the great white whale.

My God! Look at the size of her!

There we have her. Your moment has come, men!

Row faster! Faster! Watch carefully now. Stay out of her line of attack! Row!

We must get into position for throwing the harpoons, Captain.

But Captain Ahab was concentrating only on the whale and didn't hear anything else.

Faster, men, faster! She's already ours! SHE'S OURS!

Look, Mr. Starbuck. She's going to throw them over!

Turn, Captain! Turn around! Forget about the . . .

But it was too late.

25

We've got to get over there to save them. Row fast, men! They'll drown if we don't reach them quickly.

Paying no attention to the closeness of the whale, Starbuck's boat went to the spot where the whale had attacked.

Get the men aboard before she attacks again!

Good job, Starbuck! Don't go away! It's now or never!

Did you hear me, Starbuck? Let no one turn away. We must finish off Moby Dick.

This is madness, Captain! We'll never capture her!

When Captain Ahab was safely aboard Starbuck's boat . . .

My harpoon! My harpoon! Where's my harpoon, men?

Here, sir, but there is no time to use it.

No! Heavens, no!

Just then the whale surfaced again.

Follow her! We've got to get her!

Night had fallen when . . .

It would be wise to return to the PEQUOD until morning. In daylight it will be easier.

All right. Let's go back.

This cursed beast won't move around at night. I'll finish her off tomorrow!

26

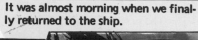

It was almost morning when we final-ly returned to the ship.

Hail, watchman! Do you see anything?

Nothing, sir. But the last time I saw her, she was headed that way.

Fedallah is missing, sir. He must have disap-peared when the whale attacked. I'm afraid......

Fedallah dead! Oh, no, not Fedallah! I can't believe it!

As the sun came up we saw we were just a short way from the whale.

She's in front of us.

Launches into the water, Starbuck. She won't escape today!

A little later . . .

Go on! Go on! Don't be afraid, men!

Look, Captain, at all the harpoons already sticking in her!

Think of all the ships that have chased her, but I'm the one who will kill her!

Captain Ahab's boat was the first one to reach the monster.

Give it to her, Queequeg! Get her good!

27

The sight we saw then made us all shake with fear and dread.

Look what she's carrying on her side.

FEDALLAH!

Yes, it's Fedallah. He must have become tangled up with the ropes from the harpoons yesterday.

The oracle was right, Fedallah. You went before me and your coffin was not made with human hands.

For a moment the whale went under, but when she came up . . .

Captain! Forget your crazy idea and let us return to the ship!

Here I am. Help me aboard, men.

Stubb's boat came to pick him up.

A harpoon! Quick! Give me a harpoon!

28

Captain, this is madness! Stop! Turn back!

I stayed on the board to keep afloat and tried to convince the captain to stop. Then . . .

My God! What could have happened to Queequeg and the rest?

CAREFUL, CAPTAIN, CAREFUL!

Take that, monster!

But the whale, made crazy from pain . . .

You haven't beat me yet, Moby Dick!

This harpoon is for you, too.

No, Captain! Forget the harpoon! Here, grab this wood!

Look how I sink my iron into you! DIE! DIE CURSED MOBY DICK!

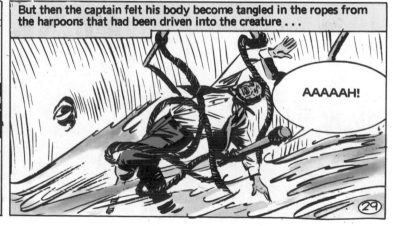

But then the captain felt his body become tangled in the ropes from the harpoons that had been driven into the creature . . .

AAAAAH!

In an instant the whale turned and noticed the closeness of the PEQUOD.

WE'RE DONE FOR!

She'll throw us over!

I closed my eyes so I wouldn't have to see what happened next.

CRAS!

From my piece of wood, unable to do a thing, I watched the terrible end of the story of Captain Ahab and his ship.

That's Queequeg's coffin! It's water tight and will stay afloat.

Thanks to that dreadful but lucky discovery, I lived on the sea several days until . . .

AHOY! You there on the boat! Help me!

I was saved by the whaler. In its search for victims of the PEQUOD, it found only one.

But my memory of the event lives on. I will never forget Queequeg, the men or Captain Ahab and the strange madness which brought him to his death.

THE END.